A TOM & RICKY MYSTERY

The Treasure Map Mystery

Bob Wright

High Noon Books
Novato, California

Series Editor: Jim Arena
Developmental Editors: Steve Shea and Elly Rabben

Book Design and Art Direction: Lucy Nielsen
Cover and Interior Illustrations: Patrick Faricy

International Standard Book Number: 978-1-57128-553-9

23 22 21 20 19 18 17
13 12 11 10 09 08 07 06 05

HighNoonBooks.com

Set 1 #8551-5
The Treasure Map Mystery #8553-9

Contents

CHAPTER 1

The Treasure Map

Ricky and Patches were in the yard. Ricky was cutting the grass.

Tom rode his bike to Ricky's house. He stopped when he saw Ricky. He got off the bike and ran into the yard. Tom had a box in his hand.

A dirty green car stopped down the street. It was not far from Ricky's house. Tom and Ricky did not see the car.

"Ricky, look what I have," Tom said.

Patches barked and wagged his tail.

"Hi, Tom. What's in the box?" Ricky asked.

"I can't wait to show you," Tom said.

In the box was an old drawing of a lake and a big, old house.

"It's just an old map," Ricky said.

"It's a map of Bear Lake and the land around the lake. The map shows that a treasure is hidden near a house at the lake," Tom said.

Ricky said, "Treasure? Like old coins and stuff? Let's go inside my house and put the map on a table. Then we can see it better."

"OK," Tom said.

Tom and Ricky went inside Ricky's house. Tom put the map on the table. They looked at it for a long time.

"You were right, Tom. This is a map of Bear

Lake. It shows where a treasure is," Ricky said.

"Isn't it cool?" Tom asked.

"Where did you get this map?" Ricky asked.

"It was in a chest my mom bought this morning. I was with her," Tom said.

"She just bought the chest this morning?" Ricky asked.

"She did. Then a man in a white hat said he would pay her for it," Tom said.

"Why?" Ricky asked.

"I don't know. He said he would pay her a lot," Tom said.

"How much?" Ricky asked.

"He said he would pay her more than she paid for the chest. He just said he had to have

"Where did you get this map?" Ricky asked.

the chest. He was very mad when my mom didn't sell it," Tom said.

"Ricky, do you think a treasure is really hidden at Bear Lake?" Tom asked

"Maybe," Ricky said.

"Do you think we could find it?" Tom asked.

Ricky said, "Maybe we can. The map shows the treasure next to a tree near a big house. I've seen that house before. I think we can find it."

"I know we can find it," Tom said.

"My dad is here. Let's show the map to him," Ricky said.

"OK," Tom said.

Tom and Ricky did not see the dirty green car. It was still parked near Ricky's house.

CHAPTER 2

The Map

Tom and Ricky saw Ricky's dad in the yard. Tom had the box and the map with him.

"Dad, look at what Tom has," Ricky said.

"What?" Ricky's dad asked.

"Show him, Tom," Ricky said.

Tom showed the box to Ricky's dad.

Ricky's dad saw what was inside the box. He asked, "Is that a map?"

"It is. It's a map of Bear Lake," Ricky said.

"It shows where a treasure is hidden," Tom said.

Ricky's dad lifted the treasure map out of the box. He held it up to look at it. He spent a long time reading all the names on the map.

"What do you think, Dad? Do you think a treasure is really hidden at Bear Lake?" Ricky asked.

"Maybe it is a treasure map. But it could be a very old drawing," Ricky's dad said.

"But a treasure might be near Bear Lake," Tom said.

"What do you think, Dad?" Ricky asked.

"Yes, it might be. Where did you get this map, Tom?" Ricky's dad asked.

"It was in a chest. My mom bought the chest this morning," Tom said.

Ricky's dad looked at the map. He pointed to one part of the map. Then he said, "The name of the artist was A. G. Stone. His name is on this drawing. I think I know that name."

Ricky's dad went in the house. He turned on his laptop. On his laptop he typed the name of the artist.

"Here it is, A. G. Stone. He was born 50 years ago. He drew many things. People pay a lot of money for his drawings," he said.

Ricky sat by the laptop. "What does it say about a treasure map?" he asked.

"The website tells about A. G. Stone's life and his drawings. But no treasure map," Ricky's dad said.

"Dad, will you take us to Bear Lake? We want to find the treasure," Ricky said.

"OK, Ricky. I'll take you and Tom to the lake. You can look for the treasure and I'll fish," his dad said.

"This is great!" Tom said.

"But you have to call your mom first, Tom. Ask her if you can go," Ricky's dad said.

"OK," Tom said.

Ricky's dad gave the map and the box to Tom.

Tom put the map in the box. Then Tom called his mom. She said it was OK for Tom to go to the lake with Ricky and his dad.

"Tom asked his mom. She said it's OK for Tom to go with us," Ricky said.

"Good. Get in the car. Come on, Patches," Ricky's dad said.

Ricky's dad got his fishing pole. Then he got in the car. Tom and Ricky and Patches got in the car, too. Tom had the box with the treasure map.

Then they left for Bear Lake.

After they left, the dirty green car left, too. It drove in back of their car.

CHAPTER 3

The House on the Map

It seemed to take a long time to drive to Bear Lake.

"Dad, when will we get to the lake?" Ricky asked.

"Just a little longer, Ricky. Don't be in such a hurry. The lake will still be there when we get to it," Ricky's dad said.

"But Tom and I want to look for the treasure," Ricky said.

"You still have lots of time," his dad said.

They rode for a little longer. The dirty green

car stayed in back of their car. But no one thought

about it.

"I see the lake," Ricky yelled.

"I see it, too. There it is! I didn't think we were going to get here," Tom said.

Patches wagged his tail and barked.

Ricky's dad stopped the car near a store next to the lake. He said, "I'm going to fish behind the store. You boys have fun. I hope you find the treasure."

Tom and Ricky and Patches got out of the car. They started to walk down the road that went around the lake. Tom had the box with the map in it.

The dirty green car stopped at the side of the

road. A man with a white hat got out. He could see Tom and Ricky. But they did not see him.

"This is great! I hope we can find the treasure," Tom said.

"I think we can. I've seen that big house. It isn't very far from here," Ricky said.

"I hope not. I'm tired," Tom said.

"You don't like to walk," Ricky said.

"I like to ride my bike," Tom said.

The man with the white hat was in back of the boys. He stayed far in back of them. They did not see him.

"Look, Tom. I see that big house," Ricky yelled to his friend.

The house had a lot of trees around it. Tom

and Ricky could see that it was like the big house on the map.

Tom stopped near the house. He said, "I think this is the big house on the map. Let's go to the house and see if any people are there."

"OK," Ricky said.

Tom and Ricky went to the house. Patches went with them.

A man's voice said, "Stop right there, boys. Don't move."

The man with the white hat hid in back of a tree when he saw the other man.

CHAPTER 4

Mr. Hill

Tom and Ricky stopped. They didn't move. Patches started barking.

"Sit, Patches," Ricky said.

Patches sat down and stopped barking.

"Turn around," the same voice said.

Tom and Ricky turned around. They saw an older man standing there.

"Who are you?" the man asked. He sounded angry.

"I'm Ricky. This is my friend Tom and my dog Patches. Who are you?" Ricky said.

15

"I'm Mr. Hill," the man said.

"Mr. Who?" Tom asked.

"I'm Mr. Hill. This is my land. Why are you boys here?" the man said.

"Is this your house? Is it your yard, too?" Ricky asked.

"Why?" Mr. Hill asked.

"We think a treasure may be hidden in your back yard," Tom said.

Mr. Hill smiled. Then he said, "So that is why you boys are here. Who said a treasure was hidden in my back yard?"

"No one. We have a map. The map shows a treasure here," Ricky said.

"Let me see the map," Mr. Hill said.

"*Let me see the map,*" Mr. Hill said.

Tom took the map out of the box. Then he gave the map to Mr. Hill.

Mr. Hill held the map for a long time. Then he said, "This is a good drawing of my house."

"Yes, it is. And it shows where the treasure is hidden in your back yard," Tom said.

"Where did you get this map?" Mr. Hill asked.

"I found it inside a chest my mom bought," Tom said.

"Can Tom and I go in your back yard? We want to try to find the treasure," Ricky asked.

"OK. I'll show you the way," Mr. Hill said. He gave the map back to Tom.

Tom and Ricky and Mr. Hill went into his

back yard. Patches went with them. There were a lot of trees in the back yard.

"Do you think we can find the right tree?" Tom asked.

"I know we can," Ricky said.

Ricky held the map up. He pointed to a tree on the map. "That's the tree next to Mr. Hill!" he said.

"That's it! And the fence next to it is also on the map," Tom said.

Tom and Ricky did not see the man with the white hat. He was hiding next to a tree.

"I think I can find the place where the treasure is hidden," Ricky said.

"I think I can, too," Tom said.

"Come on. Let's look," Ricky said.

The boys went to where they thought the treasure was hidden. It was near another very big tree.

"This is the place," Ricky said.

"I hope so," Tom said.

Ricky turned to Mr. Hill. He said, "Tom and I think the treasure is next to this tree. Can we dig a big hole here?"

"No. You can't dig a hole here," Mr. Hill said.

CHAPTER 5

Hidden Treasure

The boys stared at Mr. Hill. He would not let them dig for the treasure. Why not?

"Why can't we dig? You saw the map. There may be a treasure hidden here. You could have a lot of money," Tom said.

"There isn't any treasure there," Mr. Hill said.

"How do you know there isn't?" Ricky asked.

"My dad found the treasure a long time ago. He dug it up. I was the same age as you two boys at that time. I saw my father dig a hole here," Mr. Hill said.

"What kind of treasure did he find?" Tom asked.

"A big box of silver coins," Mr. Hill said.

"Why don't people know about the box of silver coins?" Ricky asked.

"That's because it's an old story. People around here forgot about it," the man said.

"I hoped we were going to find the treasure," Tom said.

"I did, too. But we found the place where the treasure was hidden," Ricky said.

"I'm glad your dad found the silver coins," Tom said to Mr. Hill.

"Thanks, boys. I'm glad I saw the map again," Mr. Hill said.

"Again? What do you mean?" Ricky asked.

"Have you seen my map before?" Tom asked.

"Yes. I met the artist who made the drawing. He came here to see my back yard. He came to see where my father dug up the treasure. He showed me the drawing," Mr. Hill said.

Tom put his map in the box. "Thank you. It was fun to look around," Tom said to Mr. Hill.

The boys and Patches went out to the road. Then they went back to where Ricky's dad was fishing.

They didn't see that the man with the white hat was in back of them.

CHAPTER 6

The Map Is Stolen

Soon Tom and Ricky were at the store. Ricky's dad was still fishing.

"Ricky, I'm going to put my map in your dad's car," Tom said.

"OK," Ricky said.

Tom went up the little hill. He put the box with the map inside the car. Then he and Ricky ran to the lake where Ricky's dad was fishing. Patches ran with them.

"Hi, boys. Look at my fish," Ricky's dad said. He had three big fish next to him.

"Wow! Those are big fish!" Tom said.

"Where is the chest with the map, Tom?" Ricky's dad asked.

"I put it in your car," Tom said.

"Maybe you should get it, Tom. Don't leave things in a car. They might get stolen," Ricky's dad said.

"It's OK to leave the map in the car. No one is going to take it," Tom said.

Ricky's dad said, "If you think so, Tom. You can do what you want to do. It's your map. Did you find the big house on the map?"

"Yes. We found it," Ricky said.

"Did you find the place where the treasure was hidden?" Ricky's dad asked.

"Yes," Ricky said.

"You don't seem very happy about it," Ricky's dad said.

"The treasure wasn't there," Tom said.

"I didn't think it was there. I didn't think it was a real treasure map," Ricky's dad said.

"But it was," Tom said.

"What do you mean?" Ricky's dad asked.

"The treasure was hidden there. We met Mr. Hill. His house is on the map. And the treasure was hidden in his yard. Years ago, he saw his father dig up a box of silver coins there," Ricky said.

"I didn't know a treasure was found at Bear Lake," Ricky's dad said.

"That's because people forgot about it," Tom said.

Patches started barking. He barked louder and louder. Ricky turned around. He saw a man with a white hat near his dad's car. The man was taking Tom's box out of the car.

"Get away from my dad's car!" Ricky yelled at the man.

The man took the map out of the box. Then he dropped the box. He ran to his dirty green car with Tom's map.

Patches chased the man. The man got in his car and drove away.

CHAPTER 7

A Big Surprise

Patches ran after the green car. "Come back, Patches!" Ricky yelled.

Patches turned around and ran back to Ricky. Ricky's dad ran to Ricky and Tom.

"You were right. I should not have left my map in your car. Now that man stole my map," Tom said to Ricky's dad.

"Maybe we can get the map. Come on, Dad. Let's chase the man in the green car. We can get him," Ricky said.

"No, Ricky. He's going too fast. I'm not

Patches ran after the green car.
"Come back, Patches!" Ricky yelled.

going to race him. People might get hurt," Ricky's dad said.

"I don't get it. I saw that man this morning. He asked my mom to sell him the chest. But she would not sell it to him. He was very mad. Do you think he knew the map was in the chest?" Tom asked.

"I think he did," Ricky said.

"Me, too. But why did he know the map was in there?" Tom asked.

"I don't know," Ricky said.

"Why would he want the map? The treasure isn't there now," Tom said.

"I think we should tell Officer Collins," Ricky said.

"I think we should, too," Tom said.

"Boys, you wait here. I'm going to the lake to get my fish. Then we'll go see Officer Collins," Ricky's dad said.

Ricky's dad went to the lake.

Patches barked and wagged his tail.

"Why are you barking, Patches?" Ricky said.

Tom and Ricky turned around to see why Patches was barking. Officer Collins was standing there! And he had a lot of fish.

"Officer Collins, why are you here?" Ricky asked.

"This is my day off. I came here to fish," Officer Collins said.

"We're glad to see you. We were going to

call you when we got back to Ricky's house," Tom said.

"Why?" Officer Collins asked.

"A man in a dirty green car stole my treasure map," Tom said.

"A man stole your treasure map?" Officer Collins asked.

"Yes, I found it inside a chest my mother bought this morning," Tom said.

"Tell me more," Officer Collins said.

"The map was a drawing that an artist made. It showed a house here at Bear Lake. And it showed where a treasure was hidden," Tom said.

"We asked my dad to bring us here. We came here to find the house," Ricky said.

"And to find out about the treasure hidden near the house," Tom said.

"But the man stole the map before you could?" Officer Collins asked.

"No. We found the place where the treasure was hidden, but it wasn't there," Tom said.

"It's Mr. Hill's house. His dad found the treasure years ago," Ricky said.

"I wish I knew why the man stole my map. The treasure isn't there any more. Who would want a treasure map like that?" Tom said.

"Maybe there is another kind of treasure in the map," Officer Collins said.

"What do you mean?" Tom asked.

"Some people pay a lot of money for art.

Maybe people would pay a lot for the map. Have you seen the man around here before?" Officer Collins asked.

"I saw him this morning. He asked my mom to sell him the chest this morning. He got very mad when she didn't sell it. I think he knew the map was in the chest," Tom said.

"Maybe he waited all day for you to put the map down. As soon as you put it down, he stole it. Did the artist write his name on the drawing?"

"Yes. Mr. Hill might know him," Tom said.

Then Officer Collins said, "I think we should go see Mr. Hill."

CHAPTER 8

The Real A. G. Stone

Ricky's dad was in his car. He said, "Come on, boys. Let's go."

"Dad, look who was fishing here," Ricky said.

Ricky's dad said, "Hi, Officer Collins. I see you caught a lot of fish."

Officer Collins said, "Yes. I was lucky. But I think the boys were not as lucky. Tom said a man stole his map. I am going to see Mr. Hill. Maybe he can tell me why a man would steal that map. The boys can show me his house, if that's OK with you."

"Is it OK for us to go with him? Then he can take us home," Ricky asked.

"It's OK, boys. I will see you at home. Thanks, Officer," Ricky's dad said.

Tom and Ricky got in Officer Collins's car.

"Patches, you stay with Dad. We'll be back in a little while," Ricky said.

Very soon they were at Mr. Hill's house. Mr. Hill was in his yard.

Tom saw a dirty green car. It was driving away from Mr. Hill's house.

"Look!" Tom said.

"What?" said Officer Collins.

"Is that the same dirty green car?" Tom asked.

"It is! What's going on?" Ricky said.

"Let's find out," said Officer Collins.

Tom, Ricky, and Officer Collins got out of the car.

Mr. Hill saw Tom and Ricky with Officer Collins. "Hi, boys. It's nice to see you again so soon," he said.

"A man stole my map," Tom said.

Mr. Hill did not say a word.

"This is Officer Collins. He knows about the map," Tom said.

"How can I help you, Officer Collins?" Mr. Hill asked.

"The boys said the artist wrote his name on the map. Can you tell me his name?" Officer Collins asked.

"I think it's A. G. Stone," he said in a low voice.

"I know about A. G. Stone. People pay a lot of money for his drawings. I think that's why the man stole Tom's map. I need to call the police station," Officer Collins said.

Officer Collins went to his car. He called the station. Mr. Hill went with him. Tom and Ricky stayed in the yard.

"I hope I get my map back. We didn't find the silver coins. But maybe people will want to pay me for the map," Tom said.

"I hope you get it back, too," Ricky said.

Very soon Officer Collins and Mr. Hill came back.

"I called the police station. They know the map was stolen. Also, they are going to look for the dirty green car," Officer Collins said.

"Thank you, Officer Collins," Tom said.

"I have some bad news for you, Tom. We think that the map was stolen from an art show before you found it. We'll know when we find the map," the officer said.

"What? That map is mine. It was in the box," Tom said.

"I have some more news. It's about Mr. Hill," Officer Collins said.

Officer Collins looked at Mr. Hill.

Mr. Hill said to Tom, "That map is not yours. It's my map. I'm A. G. Stone."

Tom and Ricky didn't know what to say.

"Is the map in your house?" Officer Collins asked.

"It is. I just bought it from the man in the green car," Mr. Hill said.

"Why?" Ricky asked.

"I made the map a long time ago. Then I lost it. It means a lot to me," Mr. Hill said.

"Why did the man in the green car take it?" Tom asked.

"I asked him to steal it from the art show. I feel very bad about it. But I just wanted my drawing," Mr. Hill said.

"I have to take you to the station," Officer Collins said to Mr. Hill.

Officer Collins drove Tom and Ricky back to Ricky's house. Then he drove Mr. Hill to the police station.

CHAPTER 9

The Rest of the Story

It was a few days later. Tom and Ricky saw a police car driving on the street. The car stopped near Ricky's house. Officer Collins got out of the car.

Tom and Ricky and Patches ran to the car.

"Officer Collins, did you find the man in the green car?" Ricky asked.

"Yes, Ricky. He was the one who stole the map from an art show," Officer Collins said.

"Why was it in the chest?" Ricky asked.

"The man in the green car put the map in

the chest so the police would not find it. He planned to pay for the chest and get the map back. But Tom's mother bought it first," Officer Collins said.

"What about Mr. Hill?" Ricky asked.

"You mean Mr. Stone. He has his map now," Officer Collins said.

"His map? But he had that man steal it from the art show!" Ricky said.

"Mr. Stone broke the law. But he does not have to go to jail. He is going to pay to make things better," Officer Collins said.

"How much money will he have to pay?" Tom asked.

"He will pay with his art. He will make a new

painting, and give it to the art show," Officer Collins said.

"I see! It's like a trade. Mr. Stone gets his map. The art show gets a new painting by Mr. Hill," Tom said.

"You mean Mr. Stone," Ricky said.

"You know what I mean," Tom said.